Gospel Hope Journal

A 12-week Bible Study Journal on Living in Light of God's Character

by Cindy M. Knight

This journal belongs to:

_____

Gospel Hope Journal

Trees and landscape images from Gordon Johnson on Pixabay

First Printing September 2021. Printed in the United States of America

ISBN: 978-1-7362058-0-8

Find more resources on my website: www.cindymknight.com

To my readers, may you know the love of your Father in heaven and serve Him faithfully.

To the Church, may we be faithful in following God, our maker and King.

To our missional community, current and past, may you always seek Him. Thank you for pursuing God with us.

To my family, thank you for practicing these questions with me, and for your support and encouragement to write this journal.

To my faithful God, the one who gave me the words for this book, and my very breath. May the glory be Yours.

Table of Contents

CREATE YOUR OWN TABLE OF CONTENTS

Write down "aha" moments of truth where God has taught you something new or memorable and enter the page number below to create your own table of contents.

Foreword by Jeff Vanderstelt

The four questions in this book sound simple, yet, if engaged with an openness to God's Spirit, can be absolutely life changing:

Who is God?
What has He done?
Who am I?
What should I do?

Far too often people read the Scriptures only asking: *What do they say?* and *What should I do?* Sadly, this leads to a humanistic morality, making God's Word all about us and subsequently, our identity all about what we do. This leads us into worldly thinking that I am what I do, and that my identity is in my performance. The beauty of the Gospel is that we are not what we do. We are who we are because of who God is and what He has done in Jesus Christ. Our identity is established from God's being and doing. And, when our identity is rightly founded on who God is and what God has done in Jesus Christ, we will walk as imitators of God as God's dearly loved children.

In light of this worldly tendency, I developed this framework of four questions, which I have taught for many years now. I have continued to experience my own personal transformation as I read God's word applying these questions, and I found that it resonates with people very deeply as the questions help us look to someone far greater than ourselves, Jesus!

I first met Cindy and her husband 20 years ago when our families both lived in Seattle. I was excited when she first told me about this book, as it takes these simple core concepts and provides an accessible, everyday tool for applying key truths about God in tangible ways to your own heart and life.

As you go through this journal, invite God's Spirit to show you the truth of what you believe about God and yourself, and how your actions might reveal what you *are believing* – rightly or wrongly. The fruit of your actions and attitudes always reveal the roots of your beliefs about God. As you practice over and over the process Cindy has laid out, you will find yourself moving from just information you know in your head to transformation you experience in your life.

May you be satisfied, strengthened, and sustained as you allow God's heart and His word to permeate your life in new and deeper ways. I am so excited to hear how God uses this tool in your life as you follow Him. May you never be the same.

—Jeff Vanderstelt
Founder and Visionary Leader of Saturate and the Soma family of churches
Author of *Saturate*, *Gospel Fluency*, and *Making Space*

INTRODUCTION

Dear Friend,

Thank you for choosing this book. God is taking me on a journey of learning to love Him and His heart, and to trust Him amid the unknown. Will you allow Him to take you on a journey as well?

When I first heard our friend and former pastor Jeff Vanderstelt share these four questions, they sounded so simple:

> *Who is God?*
> *What has He done?*
> *Who am I?*
> *What should I do?*

I began to journal through Scripture using these four questions and realized these seemingly easy questions are truly profound. They have caused me to reframe the way I view God, others, and myself. The focus in Scripture is God. He is the creator who spoke the world into being, the great "I am" who called to Moses from the burning bush, the innocent Son of God who willingly died in our place that we might live and be truly free, and He is the one who is coming back to make all things new.

Using these questions, we began to study through Scripture in groups at our church and in the community, and with family, friends, and neighbors. People are finding strength as they look to God to be their redeemer, deliverer, strength, and refuge. And through this work, God is drawing me into a deeper understanding of who He is and He is teaching me to find my identity in who He says I am.

Last year, I started journaling through the Psalms—one of my favorite books of the Bible—to further explore these questions. That's when God began to grow the idea of this journal in me, but He told me, "Not yet." We walked through difficulties on multiple fronts at the same time. Challenges with kids, business changes, family relationship dynamics, church transitions, and the list goes on. Some months later, God released me to write, and the words simply poured out.

Through these questions, God is showing me time after time that He is steadfast, faithful, and true. His works are too many to count: He provides, He hears and answers when we call, and He satisfies. He calls us to remember His works and to speak about them to future generations. He calls me to be a dependent worshiper of Him, and to rest in Him. I fail often in these areas, but He keeps seeking me and calling me into relationship with Him, and patiently teaches me. God is teaching me to cry out to Him when circumstances are hard and I know I need Him, and He is teaching me to look to Him also when things are good and I forget to focus on Him.

Through this journal, I pray that your eyes will focus on the good, glorious, great, and gracious God that desires a relationship with you. When you focus your eyes on the God who sees you, loves you, and is more than enough for every situation you face in life, may your heart be captured by affection for Him, and may He draw you closer to His heart through every page.

Let me know how this journey goes for you; I would love to hear from you about what God is doing in your heart and life. You can find more information on how to connect with me and with others on my website: www.cindymknight.com. Process what you're learning each week with others—your family, friends, small group, or neighbors. Discuss the practical application steps together and consider reading one or more of the recommended books (some are even available on the free Hoopla or Libby library reading apps).

Ask God what next steps He has for you. Then take a step of faith and do what He is telling you to do. You will be so glad you did.

To the faithful one, may the glory be His!

With much love,

Cindy

How to use this journal

This 12-week book combines daily journal pages and a weekly devotional. It is set up for you to journal five days during the week, go through the devotional on the sixth day, and have one day off or as a catch-up day.

Journal Pages: Each of the journal pages is the same, with the exception of the Bible verse at the bottom of the page. These pages are meant for you to dig into learning what the Bible has to say about God and your relationship to Him.

1. Choose a book of the Bible, and journal through a section or a chapter at a time. New to Bible study or not sure where to start? I recommend going through a chapter in the Psalms every day.

2. Read through the passage you have chosen in your Bible (Psalm 1 is shown in the example below). If you prefer to read the Bible on a screen, there are great websites (i.e. www.biblegateway.com) and apps (i.e. YouVersion).

3. Consider the four questions in relation to your chosen Scripture passage. You can do this after you read the passage, or go through these questions and write out the answers while you read:
Who is God? What has He done? Who am I? What should I do?

   Write the answers you find in each column. Ask God to show you what is true of His character and works, your identity in Him, and how you should live in light of this.

Example of answers for Psalm 1:

Who is God?	What has He done? (especially in the person/work of Jesus)	Who am I?	What should I do?
LAWGIVER ALL-PRESENT	GIVES THE LAW AND FREEDOM FROM THE LAW WATCHES OVER THE WAYS OF THE RIGHTEOUS	WORSHIPER FRUITFUL	DELIGHT IN THE LAW OF THE LORD MEDITATE ON HIS LAW BOTH DAY AND NIGHT REST IN GOD AS LIVING WATER

As we ask these four questions while reading the Bible, we see God for who He really is, and our hearts are softened toward Him and His glory. The way we view ourselves and our identity changes in light of these truths, and we see ourselves through God's eyes and who He is making us to be. The way we see our work changes as we rest in Jesus' completed work on the cross. We are satisfied, strengthened, and sustained as we allow God's heart and His word to permeate our lives.

Here are a few things to note:

- Consider that some things you read in the Bible are "prescriptive" (telling us what we should do) and other things are "descriptive" (a description of what happened, but not directing us to do things the same way). Not every description is something that should be applied to your own life (i.e. just because there is killing in the Bible doesn't mean that it is acceptable for us to do).

- Different forms of the same word can fit in more than one column (i.e. God is our redeemer, and we are redeemed). Some things God alone does for us (i.e. create in me a pure heart), and sometimes our works affect Him (i.e. we are worshipers and He is worshiped). Be creative and ask Him to teach you.

4. After you journal through the questions, look back over your notes and consider what truths God might be calling you to believe about Him and about yourself.

Example:

> **Truths I need to believe**
> - about God: HE TEACHES ME WHAT HE WANTS ME TO DO AND HOW TO PLEASE HIM.
> - about myself: I AM FREE WHEN I OBEY GOD.

5. Spend time writing your reflections from the current day's study, as well as a prayer to God.

Example:

> **Reflections:** I AM A WORSHIPER WHO DELIGHTS IN GOD'S LAW.
>
> **Prayer:** GOD, TEACH ME TO DESIRE TO OBEY YOU. HELP ME DELIGHT IN YOUR LAW.

6. Write key Scripture verses for the day that are meaningful to you and meditate on them.

Example:

Meaningful verses to me:
BUT HIS DELIGHT IS IN THE LAW OF THE LORD,
AND ON HIS LAW HE MEDITATES DAY AND NIGHT.
PSALM 1:2

7. Consider memorizing one of the verses you have chosen, or use the verse printed at the bottom of your journal page. If memorization is overwhelming, you can choose part of a verse or choose one verse to memorize for the week. Consider posting your verse in a prominent place in your house (i.e. the bathroom mirror, a cupboard door, by your desk, etc). Meditate on His word and ask God to help you know Him and His heart in a deeper way, to show you His presence, and help you fall more in love with Him every day.

Weekly Devotional Pages: The weekly devotionals are meant to help you dig deeper into different areas of your faith and relationship with God. There are questions to help you process what you're learning, and most weeks there is a place to reflect on what God is teaching you. Pray and ask God how He wants you to best apply what you are learning.

Each devotional concludes with practical application steps. The practical application section has both immediate steps you can take, as well as extended opportunities including several recommendations for books and other ways to process and practice what you're learning.

Talk over what you are learning with a friend, your small group, or a family member, and look for ways to remind each other of the gospel (good news) of Jesus. He is truly better than anything that this world offers!

> "I HAVE COME THAT THEY MAY HAVE
> LIFE, AND HAVE IT TO THE FULL."
>
> —JESUS
>
> JOHN 10:10B

Week 1 / Day 1

Date:

Scripture passage:

Who is God?	What has He done? (especially in the person/work of Jesus)	Who am I?	What should I do?

Truths I need to believe
- about God:

- about myself:

Reflections:

Prayer:

Meaningful verses to me:

After this, the word of the Lord came to Abram in a vision:
"Do not be afraid, Abram. I am your shield, your very great reward.
—Genesis 15:1

WEEK 1 / DAY 2

DATE:

SCRIPTURE PASSAGE:

Who is God?	What has He done? (especially in the person/work of Jesus)	Who am I?	What should I do?

Truths I need to believe
- about God:

- about myself:

Reflections:

Prayer:

Meaningful verses to me:

Moses answered the people, "Do not be afraid. Stand firm and you will see the deliverance the Lord will bring you today. The Egyptians you see today you will never see again. The Lord will fight for you; you need only to be still."
—Exodus 14:13-14

WEEK 1 / DAY 3

DATE:

SCRIPTURE PASSAGE:

Who is God?	What has He done? (especially in the person/work of Jesus)	Who am I?	What should I do?

Truths I need to believe
- about God:

- about myself:

Reflections:

Prayer:

Meaningful verses to me:

The Lord would speak to Moses face to face,
as one speaks to a friend.
—Exodus 33:11a

Week 1 / Day 4

Date: **Scripture passage:**

Who is God?	What has He done? (especially in the person/work of Jesus)	Who am I?	What should I do?

Truths I need to believe
- about God:

- about myself:

Reflections:

Prayer:

Meaningful verses to me:

The Lord bless you and keep you; the Lord make his face shine on you and be gracious to you; the Lord turn his face toward you and give you peace.
—Numbers 6:24-26

Week 1 / Day 5

DATE:

SCRIPTURE PASSAGE:

Who is God?	What has He done? (especially in the person/work of Jesus)	Who am I?	What should I do?

Truths I need to believe
- about God:

- about myself:

Reflections:

Prayer:

Meaningful verses to me:

*You were shown these things so that you might know
that the Lord is God; besides him there is no other.*
—Deuteronomy 4:35

GOD'S CHARACTER

Throughout Scripture, we find examples of God's character and His true and unchanging nature. He is good, glorious, gracious, and great. He is steadfast and true. The righteous judge, the faithful bridegroom, the coming King. List some of God's character traits you have seen as you journaled through Scripture this week: _____

_____

_____

_____

Through this study, what is God teaching you about His character? _____

_____

_____

Write a prayer to God reflecting on today's devotional. _____

_____

_____

PRACTICAL APPLICATION:

- Seek time alone in prayer with God. Speak His character qualities to Him in worship and praise. Ask Him to help you become more like Him in every part of your life.

- The next time you read a book or watch a movie, look for ways you see God's image shown in people or in the world. Share with a friend or family member what you are learning.

- Listen to music that focuses on the character qualities of God and thank Him for His nearness.

WEEK 2

WEEK 2 / DAY 1

DATE:

SCRIPTURE PASSAGE:

Who is God?	What has He done? (especially in the person/work of Jesus)	Who am I?	What should I do?

Truths I need to believe
- about God:

- about myself:

Reflections:

Prayer:

Meaningful verses to me:

The Lord your God will circumcise your hearts and the hearts of your descendants,
so that you may love him with all your heart and with all your soul, and live.
—Deuteronomy 30:6

Week 2 / Day 2

Date:

Scripture passage:

Who is God?	What has He done? (especially in the person/work of Jesus)	Who am I?	What should I do?

Truths I need to believe
- about God:

- about myself:

Reflections:

Prayer:

Meaningful verses to me:

You know with all your heart and soul that not one of all the good promises the Lord your God gave you has failed. Every promise has been fulfilled; not one has failed.
—Joshua 23:14b

WEEK 2 / DAY 3

DATE:

SCRIPTURE PASSAGE:

Who is God?	What has He done? (especially in the person/work of Jesus)	Who am I?	What should I do?

Truths I need to believe
- about God:

- about myself:

Reflections:

Prayer:

Meaningful verses to me:

*How great you are, Sovereign Lord! There is no one like you,
and there is no God but you, as we have heard with our own ears.*
—2 Samuel 7:22

WEEK 2 / DAY 4

DATE:

SCRIPTURE PASSAGE:

Who is God?	What has He done? (especially in the person/work of Jesus)	Who am I?	What should I do?

Truths I need to believe
- about God:

- about myself:

Reflections:

Prayer:

Meaningful verses to me:

You alone are the Lord. You made the heavens, even the highest heavens, and all their starry host, the earth and all that is on it, the seas and all that is in them. You give life to everything, and the multitudes of heaven worship you.
—Nehemiah 9:6

WEEK 2 / DAY 5

DATE:

SCRIPTURE PASSAGE:

Who is God?	What has He done? (especially in the person/work of Jesus)	Who am I?	What should I do?

Truths I need to believe
- about God:

- about myself:

Reflections:

Prayer:

Meaningful verses to me:

The Spirit of God has made me;
the breath of the Almighty gives me life.
—Job 33:4

God's works

There are so many times in Scripture where the works of God, Jesus, or the Holy Spirit are mentioned. We see many references to the Israelites' delivery from Egypt, the coming Messiah, and Jesus' work on the cross. List the most meaningful works of God you have studied this week: _____

_____

_____

_____

Through this study, what is God teaching you about His works? _____

_____

_____

Write a prayer to God reflecting on today's devotional. _____

_____

_____

Practical application:

- Take a walk outside in nature and thank God for His mighty works. Remember the works He has shown you in your reading and praise Him for the wonderful things He has done.

- As you pray by yourself or with others, start by proclaiming the truths of God's character and His works. Use this as a time of worship of our great God!

- Consider how the works of your hands reflect the work of your Father and ask Him to help you become more like Him as you work, play, rest, and create.

WEEK 3

WEEK 3 / DAY 1

DATE:

SCRIPTURE PASSAGE:

Who is God?	What has He done? (especially in the person/work of Jesus)	Who am I?	What should I do?

Truths I need to believe
- about God:

- about myself:

Reflections:

Prayer:

Meaningful verses to me:

Be strong and take heart,
all you who hope in the Lord.
—Psalm 31:24

WEEK 3 / DAY 2

DATE:

SCRIPTURE PASSAGE:

Who is God?	What has He done? (especially in the person/work of Jesus)	Who am I?	What should I do?

Truths I need to believe
- about God:

- about myself:

Reflections:

Prayer:

Meaningful verses to me:

May your unfailing love be with us, Lord,
even as we put our hope in you.
—Psalm 33:22

WEEK 3 / DAY 3

DATE:

SCRIPTURE PASSAGE:

Who is God?	What has He done? (especially in the person/work of Jesus)	Who am I?	What should I do?

Truths I need to believe
- about God:

- about myself:

Reflections:

Prayer:

Meaningful verses to me:

For what you have done I will always praise you in the presence of your
faithful people. And I will hope in your name, for your name is good.
—Psalm 52:9

Week 3 / Day 4

Date:

Scripture passage:

Who is God?	What has He done? (especially in the person/work of Jesus)	Who am I?	What should I do?

Truths I need to believe
- about God:

- about myself:

Reflections:

Prayer:

Meaningful verses to me:

For you have been my hope, Sovereign Lord,
my confidence since my youth.
—Psalm 71:5

WEEK 3 / DAY 5

DATE:

SCRIPTURE PASSAGE:

Who is God?	What has He done? (especially in the person/work of Jesus)	Who am I?	What should I do?

Truths I need to believe
- about God:

- about myself:

Reflections:

Prayer:

Meaningful verses to me:

Remember your word to your servant,
for you have given me hope.
—Psalm 119:49

MY IDENTITY IN CHRIST

We have all been given "labels" by people around us. Some might be positive labels (i.e. nice-looking, smart), while others may be neutral or even horribly damaging. Maybe these labels came from a teacher, kids at school, co-workers, your parents, or even an acquaintance. Write some of the labels people have called you. _____

_____

To whom are you looking to define your identity? As we look at Scripture in light of who God is and what He has done, we can rightly understand our true identity of who we are in Christ. What *God* says about us is most important. He even gives multiple people in the Bible a new name to reflect how He sees them. List identity statements you have seen in Scripture this week. If you need inspiration, see Ephesians 1:3-14. _____

_____

Through this study, what is God teaching you about your identity in Christ? _____

_____

Write a prayer to God reflecting on today's devotional. _____

_____

PRACTICAL APPLICATION:

- Consider the labels you are believing about yourself and ask God to speak truth into your heart. Ask Him to speak a new identity over you and show you how He sees you in Christ. Believe Him, dear one.

- Speak words of true identity to your friends. Remind them about God says about them. They are accepted, redeemed, adopted, and so much more. See your notes above and on your daily journal pages.

- Write Scriptures reminding you of the new labels God gives you on paper and post them on your desk, in your kitchen, on your bathroom mirror, in your car, and around your house. Meditate on them often.

- Read *Hello, My Name Is* by Matthew West, and consider how to seek your true identity from God.

WEEK 4

WEEK 4 / DAY 1

DATE:

SCRIPTURE PASSAGE:

Who is God?	What has He done? (especially in the person/work of Jesus)	Who am I?	What should I do?

Truths I need to believe
- about God:

- about myself:

Reflections:

Prayer:

Meaningful verses to me:

You are my refuge and my shield;
I have put my hope in your word.
—Psalm 119:114

WEEK 4 / DAY 2

DATE:

SCRIPTURE PASSAGE:

Who is God?	What has He done? (especially in the person/work of Jesus)	Who am I?	What should I do?

Truths I need to believe
- about God:

- about myself:

Reflections:

Prayer:

Meaningful verses to me:

Israel, put your hope in the Lord, for with the Lord is
unfailing love and with him is full redemption.
—Psalm 130:7

Week 4 / Day 3

Date:

Scripture passage:

Who is God?	What has He done? (especially in the person/work of Jesus)	Who am I?	What should I do?

Truths I need to believe
- about God:

- about myself:

Reflections:

Prayer:

Meaningful verses to me:

He has made everything beautiful in its time. He has also set eternity in the human heart; yet no one can fathom what God has done from beginning to end.
—Ecclesiastes 3:11

Week 4 / Day 4

Date:

Scripture passage:

Who is God?	What has He done? (especially in the person/work of Jesus)	Who am I?	What should I do?

Truths I need to believe
- about God:

- about myself:

Reflections:

Prayer:

Meaningful verses to me:

Lord, you are my God; I will exalt you and praise your name, for in perfect faithfulness you have done wonderful things, things planned long ago.
—Isaiah 25:1

29

WEEK 4 / DAY 5

DATE:

SCRIPTURE PASSAGE:

Who is God?	What has He done? (especially in the person/work of Jesus)	Who am I?	What should I do?

Truths I need to believe
- about God:

- about myself:

Reflections:

Prayer:

Meaningful verses to me:

Yet the Lord longs to be gracious to you;
therefore he will rise up to show you compassion.
—Isaiah 30:18a

OUR WORKS

When we read the Bible, what happens when we focus primarily on what we should do? When does trying to obey God become, instead, accomplishing work in our own strength? _____

_____

What happens to our priorities when we look first at God's character and works, as well as our identity in Christ, before focusing on what we should do? _____

_____

Through this study, what is God teaching you about your "doing"? _____

_____

Write a prayer to God reflecting on today's devotional. _____

_____

_____

By first looking at God's character and works, and our identity in Him, we put our "doing" into the right perspective. Some of the most profound things I have learned about my works is the importance of resting in God, being dependent on Him, and worshiping Him. When my mind is focused on God, my priorities change. My heart becomes peaceful even when circumstances are difficult. Through it all, God is faithful.

PRACTICAL APPLICATION:

- Read Ephesians 2:8-9. What is needed for us to be saved by God? What is God's part? What is our part?

- Our actions display what we truly believe in our heart. Do your actions show you believe God is enough? Or are you striving to do more to be accepted by God? Repent and turn to Him. He is more than enough!

- Ask God to help you really understand deep in your heart that through Jesus you are worthy of God's love regardless of your present or past. He loves you more than you can ever imagine.

WEEK 5

WEEK 5 / DAY 1

DATE:

SCRIPTURE PASSAGE:

Who is God?	What has He done? (especially in the person/work of Jesus)	Who am I?	What should I do?

Truths I need to believe
- about God:

- about myself:

Reflections:

Prayer:

Meaningful verses to me:

But those who hope in the Lord will renew their strength. They will soar on wings like eagles; they will run and not grow weary, they will walk and not be faint.
—Isaiah 40:31

Week 5 / Day 2

Date: **Scripture passage:**

Who is God?	What has He done? (especially in the person/work of Jesus)	Who am I?	What should I do?

Truths I need to believe
- about God:

- about myself:

Reflections:

Prayer:

Meaningful verses to me:

Though the mountains be shaken and the hills be removed, yet my unfailing love for you will not be shaken nor my covenant of peace be removed," says the Lord, who has compassion on you.
—Isaiah 54:10

Week 5 / Day 3

Date:

Scripture passage:

Who is God?	What has He done? (especially in the person/work of Jesus)	Who am I?	What should I do?

Truths I need to believe
- about God:

- about myself:

Reflections:

Prayer:

Meaningful verses to me:

No one is like you, Lord; you are great,
and your name is mighty in power.
—Jeremiah 10:6

WEEK 5 / DAY 4

DATE:

SCRIPTURE PASSAGE:

Who is God?	What has He done? (especially in the person/work of Jesus)	Who am I?	What should I do?

Truths I need to believe
- about God:

- about myself:

Reflections:

Prayer:

Meaningful verses to me:

Call to me and I will answer you and tell you
great and unsearchable things you do not know.
—Jeremiah 33:3

WEEK 5 / DAY 5

DATE:

SCRIPTURE PASSAGE:

Who is God?	What has He done? (especially in the person/work of Jesus)	Who am I?	What should I do?

Truths I need to believe
- about God:

- about myself:

Reflections:

Prayer:

Meaningful verses to me:

You came near when I called you,
and you said, "Do not fear."
—Lamentations 3:57

KEEPING OUR EYES ON JESUS

Read Matthew 14:22-36 where Jesus invites Peter to step out of the boat and walk on the water with Him.

In this story, what do we learn about:

- Who God is?_____
- What He's done? _____
- Who we are?_____
- What we should do? _____

Through this study, what is God teaching you about keeping your eyes on Jesus? _____

_____

What things represent the wind and the waves in your life that are distracting you from keeping your eyes on Jesus?

_____

What are you doing to intentionally keep your eyes on Jesus? How are people in your life pointing you to Jesus?

_____

Write a prayer to God reflecting on today's devotional. _____

_____

PRACTICAL APPLICATION:

- Pray for and actively pursue friendships with people who point you to Jesus. Praise Him both when life is good, and also when the storms of life come and life is hard.

- Listen to the song *Oceans* by Hillsong or read *Kisses from Katie* by Katie Davis, and prayerfully ask God for what new ways He wants you to step out in faith to follow Him right where you are or across the world.

WEEK 6

WEEK 6 / DAY 1

DATE:

SCRIPTURE PASSAGE:

Who is God?	What has He done? (especially in the person/work of Jesus)	Who am I?	What should I do?

Truths I need to believe
- about God:

- about myself:

Reflections:

Prayer:

Meaningful verses to me:

*I will give you a new heart and put a new spirit in you; I will remove from you
your heart of stone and give you a heart of flesh. And I will put my Spirit in you
and move you to follow my decrees and be careful to keep my laws.
—Ezekiel 36:26-27*

Week 6 / Day 2

Date: **Scripture passage:**

Who is God?	What has He done? (especially in the person/work of Jesus)	Who am I?	What should I do?

Truths I need to believe
- about God:

- about myself:

Reflections:

Prayer:

Meaningful verses to me:

But as for me, I watch in hope for the Lord,
I wait for God my Savior; my God will hear me.
—Micah 7:7

WEEK 6 / DAY 3

DATE:

SCRIPTURE PASSAGE:

Who is God?	What has He done? (especially in the person/work of Jesus)	Who am I?	What should I do?

Truths I need to believe
- about God:

- about myself:

Reflections:

Prayer:

Meaningful verses to me:

The Lord your God is with you, the Mighty Warrior who saves. He will take great delight in you;
in his love he will no longer rebuke you, but will rejoice over you with singing.
—Zephaniah 3:17

WEEK 6 / DAY 4

DATE:

SCRIPTURE PASSAGE:

Who is God?	What has He done? (especially in the person/work of Jesus)	Who am I?	What should I do?

Truths I need to believe
- about God:

- about myself:

Reflections:

Prayer:

Meaningful verses to me:

Come to me, all you who are weary and burdened, and I will give you rest.
Take my yoke upon you and learn from me, for I am gentle and humble in heart, and
you will find rest for your souls. For my yoke is easy and my burden is light.
—Matthew 11:28-30

Week 6 / Day 5

Date:

Scripture passage:

Who is God?	What has He done? (especially in the person/work of Jesus)	Who am I?	What should I do?

Truths I need to believe
- about God:

- about myself:

Reflections:

Prayer:

Meaningful verses to me:

In the beginning was the Word, and the
Word was with God, and the Word was God.
—John 1:1

THE LOVE OF THE FATHER

What is your earthly father like? _____

How do you view God, your Heavenly Father? _____

_____

Read 1 John 3 and consider what you learn about:

- Who God is? _____

- What He's done? _____

- Who we are? _____

- What we should do? _____

What does it mean to you that God has lavished His love on us (1 John 3:1)? _____

_____

Through this study, what is God teaching you about His love? _____

_____

_____

PRACTICAL APPLICATION:

- Write a prayer to God asking Him to help you know and deeply feel His lavish love for you. Ask Him to help you receive His love and give it away to others.

- Watch *The Chosen*, available on YouTube or The Chosen app in your app store. Pay special attention to the way that Jesus loves those around Him, and the way the characters receive His love.

- Read *Crazy Love* by Francis Chan, and ask God to show you His amazing, relentless love.

WEEK 7

Week 7 / Day 1

Date:

Scripture passage:

Who is God?	What has He done? (especially in the person/work of Jesus)	Who am I?	What should I do?

Truths I need to believe
- about God:

- about myself:

Reflections:

Prayer:

Meaningful verses to me:

So if the Son sets you free,
you will be free indeed.
—John 8:36

Week 7 / Day 2

Date: **Scripture passage:**

Who is God?	What has He done? (especially in the person/work of Jesus)	Who am I?	What should I do?

Truths I need to believe
- about God:

- about myself:

Reflections:

Prayer:

Meaningful verses to me:

I am the vine; you are the branches. If you remain in me and I in you,
you will bear much fruit; apart from me you can do nothing.
—John 15:5

WEEK 7 / DAY 3

DATE:

SCRIPTURE PASSAGE:

Who is God?	What has He done? (especially in the person/work of Jesus)	Who am I?	What should I do?

Truths I need to believe
- about God:

- about myself:

Reflections:

Prayer:

Meaningful verses to me:

Again Jesus said, "Peace be with you! As the Father has sent me, I am sending you."
And with that he breathed on them and said, "Receive the Holy Spirit.
—John 20:21-22

Week 7 / Day 4

DATE:	SCRIPTURE PASSAGE:

Who is God?	What has He done? (especially in the person/work of Jesus)	Who am I?	What should I do?

Truths I need to believe
- about God:

- about myself:

Reflections:

Prayer:

Meaningful verses to me:

Therefore my heart is glad and my tongue rejoices;
my body also will rest in hope.
—Acts 2:26

Week 7 / Day 5

DATE:

SCRIPTURE PASSAGE:

Who is God?	What has He done? (especially in the person/work of Jesus)	Who am I?	What should I do?

Truths I need to believe
- about God:

- about myself:

Reflections:

Prayer:

Meaningful verses to me:

After they prayed, the place where they were meeting
was shaken. And they were all filled with the
Holy Spirit and spoke the word of God boldly.
—Acts 4:31

PRAY CONTINUALLY

In the Bible, we learn that God hears our prayers, He answers us, and battles are won when we seek God's will in prayer. There are at least 334 references to prayer in the Bible. Two well-known prayers from Jesus include The Lord's Prayer in Matthew 6:9-13 and Jesus' High Priestly Prayer in John 17. The book of Acts shows a continual focus on prayer, with six references in just the first four chapters (1:14, 1:24, 2:42, 3:1, 4:24, 4:31).

What has your experience been with prayer? _____

_____

Using a tool like biblegateway.com or the YouVersion Bible app, search for the word prayer, pray, or praying. List the most meaningful verses and what you learn about prayer in these verses, and consider writing out one or more verses on 3x5 cards and placing them around your house in visible location(s): _____

_____

Through this study, what is God teaching you about prayer? _____

_____

Write a prayer to God reflecting on today's devotional. _____

_____

PRACTICAL APPLICATION:

- Incorporate "pray without ceasing" in your life. Speak quick one-sentence prayers to God throughout your day. Seek His heart and tell Him that more than anything else in this world you want to know Him more.

- Watch the movie *War Room* and ask God to show you how to deepen your prayer life and take your battles to Him in prayer throughout each day.

- Pray while you take a walk through your home, neighborhood, or community, and ask God where He is calling you to bring healing and restoration. Ask Him to show you next steps.

WEEK 8

Week 8 / Day 1

DATE:

SCRIPTURE PASSAGE:

Who is God?	What has He done? (especially in the person/work of Jesus)	Who am I?	What should I do?

Truths I need to believe
- about God:

- about myself:

Reflections:

Prayer:

Meaningful verses to me:

And hope does not put us to shame, because
God's love has been poured out into our hearts
through the Holy Spirit, who has been given to us.
—Romans 5:5

Week 8 / Day 2

Date:

Scripture passage:

Who is God?	What has He done? (especially in the person/work of Jesus)	Who am I?	What should I do?

Truths I need to believe
- about God:

- about myself:

Reflections:

Prayer:

Meaningful verses to me:

It does not, therefore, depend on human desire
or effort, but on God's mercy.
—Romans 9:16

WEEK 8 / DAY 3

DATE:

SCRIPTURE PASSAGE:

Who is God?	What has He done? (especially in the person/work of Jesus)	Who am I?	What should I do?

Truths I need to believe
- about God:

- about myself:

Reflections:

Prayer:

Meaningful verses to me:

Be joyful in hope, patient in affliction, faithful in prayer.
—Romans 12:12

WEEK 8 / DAY 4

DATE:

SCRIPTURE PASSAGE:

Who is God?	What has He done? (especially in the person/work of Jesus)	Who am I?	What should I do?

Truths I need to believe
- about God:

- about myself:

Reflections:

Prayer:

Meaningful verses to me:

May the God who gives endurance and encouragement give you the same attitude of mind toward each other that Christ Jesus had, so that with one mind and one voice you may glorify the God and Father of our Lord Jesus Christ.
—Romans 15:5-6

WEEK 8 / DAY 5

DATE:

SCRIPTURE PASSAGE:

Who is God?	What has He done? (especially in the person/work of Jesus)	Who am I?	What should I do?

Truths I need to believe
- about God:

- about myself:

Reflections:

Prayer:

Meaningful verses to me:

For the foolishness of God is wiser than human wisdom,
and the weakness of God is stronger than human strength.
—1 Corinthians 1:25

FERTILE SOIL

Read Matthew 13:1-23. List the four kinds of soil and the four kinds of responses:

1. _____

2. _____

3. _____

4. _____

How soft is the soil of your heart to God and His word today? What do your actions show that your heart believes?

_____

What does it mean to receive God's word with joy? How do we build strong roots that produce a large crop?

_____

Read a couple sections of Psalm 119. What does the Psalmist believe about God's word?_____

_____

Through this study, what is God teaching you? _____

_____

PRACTICAL APPLICATION:

- Write a prayer to God reflecting on today's devotional. Ask Him to make your heart more like His.

- Consider what friends, books, and/or podcasts are speaking into your life and feeding your soul. Are they encouraging you to follow God's heart and His word? How are you pointing other people to Jesus?

- Build a daily habit of reading God's Word and delighting in it. By spending 15 minutes a day, you can read the whole Bible in a year. Consider a daily Bible reading plan like BibleProject | The Bible on the YouVersion app, where the Bible Project videos visually explain what you are reading.

WEEK 9

WEEK 9 / DAY 1

DATE:

SCRIPTURE PASSAGE:

Who is God?	What has He done? (especially in the person/work of Jesus)	Who am I?	What should I do?

Truths I need to believe
- about God:

- about myself:

Reflections:

Prayer:

Meaningful verses to me:

So whether you eat or drink or whatever
you do, do it all for the glory of God.
—1 Corinthians 10:31

WEEK 9 / DAY 2

DATE:

SCRIPTURE PASSAGE:

Who is God?	What has He done? (especially in the person/work of Jesus)	Who am I?	What should I do?

Truths I need to believe
- about God:

- about myself:

Reflections:

Prayer:

Meaningful verses to me:

Be on your guard; stand firm in the faith;
be courageous; be strong. Do everything in love.
—1 Corinthians 16:13-14

Week 9 / Day 3

Date:

Scripture passage:

Who is God?	What has He done? (especially in the person/work of Jesus)	Who am I?	What should I do?

Truths I need to believe
- about God:

- about myself:

Reflections:

Prayer:

Meaningful verses to me:

He has delivered us from such a deadly peril, and he will deliver us again. On him we have set our hope that he will continue to deliver us, as you help us by your prayers.
—2 Corinthians 1:10-11a

Week 9 / Day 4

Date:

Scripture passage:

Who is God?	What has He done? (especially in the person/work of Jesus)	Who am I?	What should I do?

Truths I need to believe
- about God:

- about myself:

Reflections:

Prayer:

Meaningful verses to me:

Therefore, if anyone is in Christ, the new creation has come:
The old has gone, the new is here!
—2 Corinthians 5:17

WEEK 9 / DAY 5

DATE:

SCRIPTURE PASSAGE:

Who is God?	What has He done? (especially in the person/work of Jesus)	Who am I?	What should I do?

Truths I need to believe
- about God:

- about myself:

Reflections:

Prayer:

Meaningful verses to me:

But the fruit of the Spirit is love, joy, peace, forbearance, kindness, goodness, faithfulness, gentleness and self-control. Against such things there is no law.
—Galatians 5:22-23

ARMOR UP!

Read Ephesians 6:10-20. List the armor of God, and what each piece is meant to accomplish: _____

_____

_____

Pray and ask God to show you on which piece of the armor He wants you to focus: _____

Select the word that is connected with your piece of armor (truth, righteousness, gospel, peace, faith, salvation, spirit), and do a word search on biblegateway.com or on the YouVersion Bible app to see what you learn from Scripture on this topic: _____

_____

Through this study, what is God teaching you? _____

_____

Write a prayer to God reflecting on today's devotional. _____

_____

PRACTICAL APPLICATION:

- Consider God's character and works and meditate on the things you know to be true about God. Ask Him to remind you often of these truths.

- Ask God to renew your mind as you soak in God's word. Consider applying a new spiritual discipline: read through the entire Bible, pray using Bible verses as a template for your prayers, memorize Scripture, or fast (take a meal or day off food and use that extra time to pray). Ask God to teach you something new about His heart and His character, and to help you obey what He is teaching you.

- Team up with a friend to pray for God's help in putting on your selected piece of armor throughout each day. Check back with that friend later in the week to encourage each other.

WEEK 10

WEEK 10 / DAY 1

DATE:

SCRIPTURE PASSAGE:

Who is God?	What has He done? (especially in the person/work of Jesus)	Who am I?	What should I do?

Truths I need to believe
- about God:

- about myself:

Reflections:

Prayer:

Meaningful verses to me:

For it is by grace you have been saved, through faith—and this is not from yourselves, it is the gift of God—not by works, so that no one can boast.
—Ephesians 2:8-9

Week 10 / Day 2

Date:

Scripture passage:

Who is God?	What has He done? (especially in the person/work of Jesus)	Who am I?	What should I do?

Truths I need to believe
- about God:

- about myself:

Reflections:

Prayer:

Meaningful verses to me:

There is one body and one Spirit, just as you were
called to one hope when you were called.
—Ephesians 4:4

WEEK 10 / DAY 3

DATE:

SCRIPTURE PASSAGE:

Who is God?	What has He done? (especially in the person/work of Jesus)	Who am I?	What should I do?

Truths I need to believe
- about God:

- about myself:

Reflections:

Prayer:

Meaningful verses to me:

Follow God's example, therefore, as dearly loved children and
walk in the way of love, just as Christ loved us and gave himself up
for us as a fragrant offering and sacrifice to God.
—Ephesians 5:1-2

Week 10 / Day 4

Date: **Scripture passage:**

Who is God?	What has He done? (especially in the person/work of Jesus)	Who am I?	What should I do?

Truths I need to believe
- about God:

- about myself:

Reflections:

Prayer:

Meaningful verses to me:

Finally, brothers and sisters, whatever is true, whatever is noble, whatever is right,
whatever is pure, whatever is lovely, whatever is admirable—if anything
is excellent or praiseworthy—think about such things.
—Philippians 4:8

WEEK 10 / DAY 5

DATE:

SCRIPTURE PASSAGE:

Who is God?	What has He done? (especially in the person/work of Jesus)	Who am I?	What should I do?

Truths I need to believe
- about God:

- about myself:

Reflections:

Prayer:

Meaningful verses to me:

To them God has chosen to make known among the Gentiles the
glorious riches of this mystery, which is Christ in you, the hope of glory.
—Colossians 1:27

UNDERSTANDING THE GOSPEL

Read 1 Corinthians 15:1-8. What do we learn about the gospel? _____

_____

The gospel is the *good news* that God came to rescue us. When we turn away from our sin (repentance) and believe in the life, death, and resurrection of His son Jesus Christ (faith), God renews us through His Spirit.

The Bible shows us three tenses of this gospel reality, that we:

- *have been* saved from the penalty of sin (justification) – Romans 5:1-2
- *are being* saved from the power of sin (sanctification) – 1 Corinthians 15:2
- *will be* saved from the presence of sin (glorification) – 2 Thessalonians 1:5-10; 2 Timothy 4:7-8

Consider the three salvation tenses (past, present, future). Which is most meaningful to you right now and why?

_____

Write a prayer to God reflecting on today's devotional. _____

_____

PRACTICAL APPLICATION:

- Tell a friend what the gospel means to you and how it influences the way you live.
- Read *The Explicit Gospel* by Matt Chandler to learn more about the gospel and its implications in our life.

"In our Christian life we never 'get beyond the gospel' to something more advanced. The gospel is not the first step in a stairway of truths; rather, it is more like the hub in a wheel of truth. The gospel is not just the ABC's but the A to Z of Christianity. The gospel is not the minimum required doctrine necessary to enter the kingdom but the way we all make progress in the kingdom." – Tim Keller[1]

[1] Tim Keller, *The Centrality of the Gospel*, https://redeemercitytocity.com/articles-stories/the-centrality-of-the-gospel

WEEK 11

WEEK 11 / DAY 1

DATE:

SCRIPTURE PASSAGE:

Who is God?	What has He done? (especially in the person/work of Jesus)	Who am I?	What should I do?

Truths I need to believe
- about God:

- about myself:

Reflections:

Prayer:

Meaningful verses to me:

We remember before our God and Father your work produced by faith, your labor prompted by love, and your endurance inspired by hope in our Lord Jesus Christ.
—1 Thessalonians 1:3

Week 11 / Day 2

Date:

Scripture passage:

Who is God?	What has He done? (especially in the person/work of Jesus)	Who am I?	What should I do?

Truths I need to believe
- about God:

- about myself:

Reflections:

Prayer:

Meaningful verses to me:

But Christ is faithful as the Son over God's house. And we are his house,
if indeed we hold firmly to our confidence and the hope in which we glory.
—Hebrews 3:6

WEEK 11 / DAY 3

DATE:

SCRIPTURE PASSAGE:

Who is God?	What has He done? (especially in the person/work of Jesus)	Who am I?	What should I do?

Truths I need to believe
- about God:

- about myself:

Reflections:

Prayer:

Meaningful verses to me:

*Let us hold unswervingly to the hope we
profess, for he who promised is faithful.*
—Hebrews 10:23

Week 11 / Day 4

Date:

Scripture passage:

Who is God?	What has He done? (especially in the person/work of Jesus)	Who am I?	What should I do?

Truths I need to believe
- about God:

- about myself:

Reflections:

Prayer:

Meaningful verses to me:

Consider it pure joy, my brothers and sisters, whenever you face trials of many kinds,
because you know that the testing of your faith produces perseverance.
—James 1:2-3

WEEK 11 / DAY 5

DATE:

SCRIPTURE PASSAGE:

Who is God?	What has He done? (especially in the person/work of Jesus)	Who am I?	What should I do?

Truths I need to believe
- about God:

- about myself:

Reflections:

Prayer:

Meaningful verses to me:

But the wisdom that comes from heaven is first of all pure; then peace-loving,
considerate, submissive, full of mercy and good fruit, impartial and sincere.
—James 3:17

DEMONSTRATING AND DECLARING THE GOSPEL

What character qualities of God are most endearing to you? _____

_____

Ask God to show you one quality you can put into action to demonstrate to those around you what God is like. This could include restorer (repairing broken fences), forgiver (paying off debts), father to the fatherless (caring for orphans or foster children), and so much more. Describe the character quality and your action step here:_____

_____

As you demonstrate these qualities through gospel metaphors, give Jesus as the reason for the metaphor you are displaying. Our good, moral lives disconnected from gospel explanation will likely convince others they don't need Jesus. You might share that you are serving others because Jesus first served us, God is the restorer of broken things, or that Jesus rescued you when you were in despair. Ask God for words to explain the metaphor and point people to Jesus with your words. Note your thoughts here: _____

_____

_____

PRACTICAL APPLICATION:

- Write a prayer to God reflecting on today's devotional. Ask God for wisdom in choosing a gospel metaphor that shows His character to those around you. Join with others to demonstrate and declare the gospel as you use this metaphor with people that don't yet know Jesus.

- Read *The Gospel Comes with a House Key* by Rosaria Butterfield and ask God to help you open your home with extraordinary hospitality.

- Join with friends to read *Gospel Fluency* by Jeff Vanderstelt, and practice together becoming "fluent" in the gospel. It is important to practice the tools found in this book in community with others. Ask God to transform your heart and your life.

WEEK 12

WEEK 12 / DAY 1

DATE:

SCRIPTURE PASSAGE:

Who is God?	What has He done? (especially in the person/work of Jesus)	Who am I?	What should I do?

Truths I need to believe
- about God:

- about myself:

Reflections:

Prayer:

Meaningful verses to me:

Praise be to the God and Father of our Lord Jesus Christ! In his great mercy he has given us new birth into a living hope through the resurrection of Jesus Christ from the dead.
—1 Peter 1:3

Week 12 / Day 2

Date:

Scripture passage:

Who is God?	What has He done? (especially in the person/work of Jesus)	Who am I?	What should I do?

Truths I need to believe
- about God:

- about myself:

Reflections:

Prayer:

Meaningful verses to me:

But you are a chosen people, a royal priesthood, a holy nation,
God's special possession, that you may declare the praises of him who
called you out of darkness into his wonderful light.
—1 Peter 2:9

Week 12 / Day 3

Date:

Scripture passage:

Who is God?	What has He done? (especially in the person/work of Jesus)	Who am I?	What should I do?

Truths I need to believe
- about God:

- about myself:

Reflections:

Prayer:

Meaningful verses to me:

Cast all your anxiety on him
because he cares for you.
—1 Peter 5:7

Week 12 / Day 4

Date:

Scripture passage:

Who is God?	What has He done? (especially in the person/work of Jesus)	Who am I?	What should I do?

Truths I need to believe
- about God:

- about myself:

Reflections:

Prayer:

Meaningful verses to me:

Dear children, let us not love with words
or speech but with actions and in truth.
—1 John 3:18

Week 12 / Day 5

Date:

Scripture passage:

Who is God?	What has He done? (especially in the person/work of Jesus)	Who am I?	What should I do?

Truths I need to believe
- about God:

- about myself:

Reflections:

Prayer:

Meaningful verses to me:

For the Lamb at the center of the throne will be their shepherd; he will lead them to springs of living water. And God will wipe away every tear from their eyes.
—Revelation 7:17

LIVING AS A CHOSEN PEOPLE

As we reach the end of this study, how will you continue applying what you have learned? _____

_____

Read 1 Peter 2:4-10. Who is *the* Living Stone? _____ Who are living stones? _____

What are some new labels we are given in verse nine?_____

_____

What would it look like for us to live like a chosen people belonging to God? _____

_____

Throughout this study, what has God been teaching you?_____

_____

Write a prayer to God reflecting on what you have learned through this journal. _____

_____

_____

PRACTICAL APPLICATION:

- Consider what you have learned on this 12-week journey. Write a letter of love and thanks to God for all that He has taught you. Use these four key elements: God's character, His works, our identity, our response.

- Share what God is showing you with a friend and ask them to pray with you for wisdom and courage to take the next steps He is showing you. He is with you wherever you go.

Afterword

Dear Friend,

Thanks for traveling this journey with me. I pray that you have found God in the pages of this book, and in the pages of your Bible, and that He has drawn you closer to His heart.

Read through your notes in this journal and pay special attention to the areas where you felt God's prompting. Add these things to the "Create your own table of contents" section at the beginning of this book.

Ask God what He has for you next. Is He asking you to step out in a new area of faith? Is He asking you to continue on the path He has already shown you? Or are there some elements of both? How are you making space to listen to Him? Pray for His help in learning to follow Him well.

Continue using this Bible study method of asking the four questions outlined in this study for any passage of Scripture. You can use your own paper or get another copy of this journal.

Practice these questions with others and encourage them to know and love God with all their heart, soul, mind, and strength.

Above all, keep your eyes on Jesus. He is the best source of joy and life we could ever desire!

To Him be the glory, forever and ever. Amen.

With much love,

Cindy M. Knight

NOTES:

NOTES:

Made in USA - Crawfordsville, IN
48773_9781736205808
09.28.2021 0444